St. Clare of Montetalco School

SPARKY'S BONE

Written by Claire Daniel
Illustrated by Eldon Doty

Silver Burdett Ginn
A Division of Simon & Schuster
160 Gould Street
Needham Heights, MA 02194 - 2310

Modern Curriculum Press
A Division of Simon & Schuster
299 Jefferson Road, P.O. Box 480
Parsippany, NJ 07054 - 0480

Design and production by BIG BLUE DOT

ISBN: 0-663-59367-0 Silver Burdett Ginn
ISBN: 0-8136-0839-2 Modern Curriculum Press

1 2 3 4 5 6 7 8 9 10 SP 01 00 99 98 97 96 95

Sparky had a great big bone.
She wanted to save it.

So Sparky dug a great big hole.
She dropped the bone in the hole.
Then she put dirt on top.

The next day, Sparky could
not find her bone.
"Who stole my bone?"
asked Sparky.

Then Sparky saw Cat.
"Cat, do you have my bone?"asked Sparky.

"No," said Cat.
"But I have a pretty green mouse.
Do you want that?"

"No, thanks," said Sparky.
"I want my bone." And off she went.

"Who stole my bone?" asked Sparky.
Then she saw Frog.
"Frog, do you have my bone?" asked Sparky.

"No," said Frog.
"But I have a pretty green bug.
Do you want that?"

"No, thanks," said Sparky.
"I want my bone."
And off she went.

"Who stole my bone?" asked Sparky.
Then she saw Cow.
"Cow, do you have my bone?" asked Sparky.

"No," said Cow.
"But I have lots of pretty green grass.
Do you want that?"

"No, thanks," said Sparky.
"I want my bone."
And off she went.

"Who stole my bone?" asked Sparky.
Then she saw her mother.
"Mother, do you have my bone?" asked Sparky.

"No," said Mother.
"But I have my nice clean bone. Do you want it?"

"Yes, please!" said Sparky.
"Please let me have your bone."
And off she went.

Sparky had a nice clean bone.
She wanted to save it.
So Sparky dug a great big hole.
She dropped the nice clean bone
in the great big hole.

She heard a clink.
What was that sound?
Sparky looked in the great big hole.

Sparky did not see one bone.
She saw two!